Bess and Tess

by Jane Manners
illustrated by Baurrox

**Harcourt**

Orlando   Boston   Dallas   Chicago   San Diego

Visit *The Learning Site!*

www.harcourtschool.com

Mark was sad. He had
no friends to play with
on his granddad's farm.

2

Mark had friends back
home in the city.

3

So Mark went to see
Bess. He liked Bess
the best.

Mark's granddad was in
the barn with Bess. Mr.
Parker was there, too.

Mr. Parker lived in the
house next to the farm.
"Take a look at Bess
and her baby," he said.

Mark ran to see. There
was Bess. There was
Tess! Tess was so small.

It didn't take long for
people to come by.

"Can I see Tess?"
"Yes," said Mark.
"Come in. Take a look."

"Can we see Bess and
Tess?" two more asked.
"Yes," said Mark. "Come
on in. Take a look."
10

Mark saw all the kids
in the barn. Sometimes
things turn out just right.

Thanks to Bess and
Tess, Mark had many
new friends.